Kipper was writing a story.

"Will you check the spelling for me?" he asked Biff.

“There is no letter ‘j’ in ‘orange’,” Biff said.

“You spell ‘orange’ with a ‘g’ and an ‘e’ at the end,” added Chip.

The magic key began to glow. It was time for an adventure.

"I want to write my story!" said Kipper.

The magic took them to a very strange place.

Kipper looked around. "Where are we?" he asked. "There are letters everywhere!"

There were letters on the ground and letters in the air.

"It's a world of letters!" said Biff.

Some letters were floating high in the sky. With a flash they joined together to make the word ‘cloud’. Then they *became* a cloud.

"I've got an idea!" said Biff. Quickly she collected some letters on the ground. She started to spell a word.

Biff spelled the word ‘snack’.

There was another flash of light and the letters on the ground became a snack.

Biff picked up the letter ‘c’ and pulled a bit off the corner.

“Yum!” she said. “Try some of this. It’s cake!”

A letter ‘e’ floated down from the sky and joined the letters on the ground.

It made a new word. The word was ‘snake’.

There was a flash of light.

Then the letters became a snake. A *big* snake.

It gave the children a hungry glare.

"Run!" shouted Kipper.

The children started to run away.

The huge snake followed them with a hiss.

“I’m not sure I like this place!” said Kipper.

“Where’s the magic key?” Chip shouted to Biff. “We need to go!”

Biff looked in her pockets but the magic key was not there.

"I haven't got it," she cried. "Where can it be?"

Chip was picking up more letters from the ground. He pushed a ‘k’, an ‘e’ and a ‘y’ together to spell ‘key’.

The letters became a real key but it was not the right key.

"That won't work!" said Biff. "It's not the magic key."

Chip looked around for more letters.

"I think we need to spell the words 'magic key'," he said.

Soon Chip had all the letters except one.
"Can you see a 'g'?" he asked.

Kipper turned round. Then he ran in the direction of the huge snake. He had to dodge around it.

"Be careful!" shouted Biff.

Then Kipper reached up. He grabbed an orange from a branch on the tree behind the snake.

He pulled the orange apart.

"It's made of all the letters to spell 'orange'!" he said.

Kipper pulled out the letter ‘g’ and threw it to Chip.

“Now you can spell ‘magic key’,” he shouted.

With a flash, the words on the ground became the real magic key.

It started to glow.

"We're going home!" cried Chip.

At home Kipper looked at his notebook.

"I've got a new story to write," he said.

"And now you can spell 'orange'!" said Biff.